MEANGIRLS

MEMORABLE
MOMENTS

T0364087

Running Press
Hachette Book Group
1290 Avenue of the Americas, New York, NY 10104
www.runningpress.com
@Running_Press

First Edition: April 2019

Published by Running Press, an imprint of Perseus Books, LLC, a subsidiary of Hachette Book Group, Inc. The Running Press name and logo is a trademark of the Hachette Book Group.

ISBN: 978-0-7924-9409-5

ON
WEDNESDAYS

we *wear* `pink.`

—Karen

That's why her hair is **so big.**

IT'S FULL OF SECRETS.

—Damian

DON'T HAVE SEX.

Cause you will get pregnant *AND DIE*.

DON'T HAVE SEX IN THE MISSIONARY POSITION.

Don't have sex standing up.

JUST . . . DON'T DO IT,

PROMISE?

Okay, everybody take some rubbers.

—Coach Carr

Regina: **BUT YOU'RE, LIKE,** *really pretty*

Cady: Thank you.

Regina: So you agree?

Cady: What?

Regina: You think you're **really pretty?**

Get in
LOSER,

We're going shopping.

—Regina

There are

NO *rules*

in this house.
I'm not a
REGULAR MOM,

I'M A COOL MOM.

—Mrs. George

Okay, irregardless.
Ex-boyfriends are just,
off limits to friends.

I mean, that's just, like,
the rules of feminism!

—Gretchen

I can't go to **TACO BELL.** I'm on an *ALL-CARB* **DIET.**

God, Karen, you are *SO STUPID!*

—*Regina*

On October 3rd, he asked
me what day it was.

It's

October 3rd.

—Cady

I'm a mouse,

DUH.

—Karen

Gretchen,
stop trying to make

"FETCH" happen.

It's NOT 💋

going to happen.

—Regina

FOUR
FOR YOU,
Glen Coco.

You go,
GLEN COCO.

—Damian

IS

butter

a **carb?**

—Regina

Janis:

You smell like a

baby prostitute.

Cady:

Thanks!

Let it out,
honey.
Put it in the book.
—Gretchen

YOU CAN'T

SIT

with us

—Gretchen

I WISH WE COULD ALL get along like we used to in middle school. **I wish I could bake** a cake filled with rainbows and smiles and everyone would **eat and be happy.**

—Random Girl

SHE DOESN'T EVEN GO **HERE**

—*Damian*

This book has been bound using
handcraft methods and Smyth-sewn
to ensure durability.

The box and interior were designed
by Mackenzie Gaul.

The text was set in Futura,
Avenir, Baskerville, and
Covered By Your Grace.